How to use this book

Follow the advice, in italics, given for you on each page.
Support the children as they read the text that is shaded in cream.
Praise *the children at every step!*

Detailed guidance is provided in the Read Write Inc. Phonics Handbook

9 reading activities

Children:
Practise reading the speed sounds.
Read the green, red and challenge words for the story.
Listen as you read the introduction.
Discuss the vocabulary check with you.
Read the story.
Re-read the story and discuss the 'questions to talk about'.
Read the story with fluency and expression.
Answer the questions to 'read and answer'.
Practise reading the speed words.

Speed sounds

Consonants   *Say the pure sounds (do not add 'uh').*

f	l	m	n	r	s	v	z	sh	th	ng
ff	ll	mm	nn	rr	ss	(ve)	zz			(nk)
	le		kn							

b	c	d	g	h	j	p	qu	t	w	x	y	ch
bb	k	dd	gg			(pp)		(tt)	wh			tch
	ck											

Vowels   *Say the sounds in and out of order.*

at	hen	in	on	up	day	see	high	blow
	head					happy	find	no

zoo	look	car	for	fair	whirl	shout	boy
			door				spoil
			snore				

*Each box contains one sound but sometimes more than one grapheme. Focus graphemes are **circled**.*

Green words

t<u>hink</u> t<u>hank</u> <u>goo</u>d plump stri<u>ng</u>

w<u>ay</u> l<u>ay</u> s<u>ay</u> d<u>ay</u> m<u>ay</u> h<u>ay</u> str<u>ay</u> st<u>ay</u> K<u>ay</u> J<u>ay</u> R<u>ay</u>

Read in syllables.

Cat`kin	→	Catkin	con`tact	→	contact
happ`y	→	happy	ki<u>tt</u>`en	→	ki<u>tt</u>en
a`w<u>ay</u>	→	aw<u>ay</u>	Ma`l<u>ay</u>`a	→	Mal<u>ay</u>a
Sun`d<u>ay</u>	→	Sund<u>ay</u>	ve`ry	→	very
hol`i`d<u>ay</u>	→	holid<u>ay</u>			

Read the root word first and then with the ending.

l<u>oo</u>k	→	l<u>oo</u>king	sit	→	si<u>tt</u>ing
ha<u>ve</u>	→	havi<u>ng</u>	pr<u>ay</u>	→	pr<u>ay</u>i<u>ng</u>
pl<u>ay</u>	→	pl<u>ay</u>ed	→	pl<u>ay</u>ful

Red words

my   they   call   all   are   your   you   her   what
be   do   she   to   brother   of

Challenge word

grey

Lost

Introduction

Have you got a cat? Has it ever got lost?
Poor Kay West, in this story, has lost her cat.
Ray finds her cat in his shed with...a surprise for Kay.
The surprise means that Ray and Kay become friends.

What do you think the surprise could be?

Story written by Gill Munton
Illustrated by Tim Archbold

Vocabulary check

Discuss the meaning (as used in the story) after the children have read each word.

	definition:	sentence/phrase:
plump	fat	*Very plump, playful black cat.*
sheds	small buildings for storing things in gardens	*Will you check your sheds?*
stray	lost	*I've got a stray cat in my shed.*
hay	dried long grass	*She's sitting in a box of hay.*
Malaya	country in the East	*I am going on holiday to Malaya.*
fond	to like something	*I am very fond of them.*

Punctuation to note in this story:
1. Capital letters to start sentences and full stops to end sentences
2. Capital letters for names
3. Exclamation marks to show anger, shock and surprise
4. 'Wait and see' dots...

Lost last Sunday:

Very plump, playful black cat called Catkin.

Will you check your sheds?

If you find her, contact Kay West

at 24 Clayton Villas.

Thank you so much for looking.

Kay West

3rd May

To Kay West

I've got a stray cat in my shed.

I think it may be Catkin!

She's sitting in a box of hay,

and she looks as if she

wants to stay in it!

I will be in at six o'clock today if you want to visit.

From Ray Brooks (33 Hilltop Way)

4th May

To Ray Brooks

Hooray! Today is such a happy day! Thank you so much for finding my Catkin! It's what I was praying for!

But it was a bit of a shock to find the kittens in the box of hay with her – a black kitten and a grey kitten!
Still, I think she will be a very good mum.
By the way, I am glad to say they are all well.

From Kay West

PS I am going on holiday on Sunday to Malaya!

5th May

To Kay

I am glad Catkin and the kittens are well.

I am very fond of them.

When you go away on holiday,

will you let them all stay with me

at Hilltop Way?

From Ray

To Ray   10th May

I am having a very good

holiday in Malaya.

Are Catkin and the kittens

being good?

Do give them all a big kiss

from me!

From Kay

Mr Ray Brooks
_____

33 Hilltop Way
_____

Grays
_____

Essex
_____

20th May

To Kay

It's good to have you back!

I want to ask you if the grey kitten may stay with me
at Hilltop Way. When you were away, he lay on my bed
all day and played with a bit of string.

I think he wants to stay.

What do you say?

From Ray

PS I have called him Jay!

21st May

To Ray

Yes, the kitten may stay with you!

I'm glad you have called him Jay.

When you go on holiday

he must stay in Clayton Villas

with me, Catkin

and his brother, Ray.

(Yes, I have called my kitten Ray!)

From Kay

Questions to talk about

Re-read the page. Read the question to the children. Tell them whether it is a **FIND IT** question or **PROVE IT** question.

FIND IT

✓ Turn to the page

✓ Read the question

✓ Find the answer

PROVE IT

✓ Turn to the page

✓ Read the question

✓ Find your evidence

✓ Explain why

Page 9:	FIND IT	What has Kay West lost?
Page 10:	FIND IT	What does Ray Brooks write to Kay West?
Page 11:	PROVE IT	Do you think this is a good time for Kay to go on holiday?
Page 12:	FIND IT	What does Ray offer to do for Kay?
Page 13:	PROVE IT	Why does this page look different from the others?
Page 14:	PROVE IT	Why does Ray choose the grey kitten rather than the black one?
Page 15:	PROVE IT	Why does Kay call her kitten Ray?

Questions to read and answer

(Children complete without your help.)

1. Where was Catkin sitting?
   Catkin was sitting in **a box of hay / a red bag / a big cup.**

2. Where did Kay go?
   Kay went to **stay with her mum / on holiday / to the shops.**

3. Where did Catkin and the kittens stay when Kay was away?
   They stayed with **gran / dad / Ray.**

4. What did the grey kitten play with?
   The grey kitten played with **a frog / a teddy / a bit of string.**

5. What are the kittens called?
   The kittens are called **Tom and Fred / Jay and Ray / Pat and Sid.**

Speed words

Children practise reading the words across the rows, down the columns and in and out of order clearly and quickly.

them	much	happy	kitten	having
looking	say	day	today	holiday
stay	away	they	are	my
called	me	being	going	she's